KT-578-965

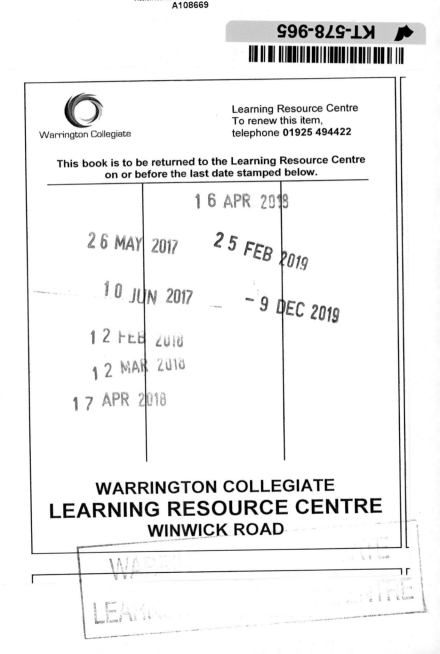

With special thanks to our reader:
Thomas Keller

First published in 2009 in Great Britain by
Barrington Stoke Ltd
18 Walker St, Edinburgh, EH3 7LP

www.barringtonstoke.co.uk

Title ISBN: 978-1-84299-714-7
Pack ISBN: 978-1-84299-789-5

Printed in Great Britain by The Charlesworth Group

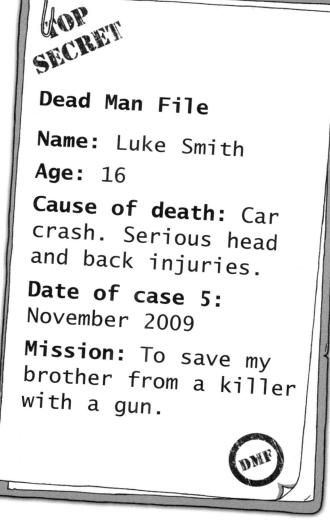

Dead Man File

Name: Luke Smith

Age: 16

Cause of death: Car crash. Serious head and back injuries.

Date of case 5: November 2009

Mission: To save my brother from a killer with a gun.

DMF

Contents

Intro

Luke Smith was killed in a car driven by his best mate, Joe. But that was not the end of it. Luke comes back as a ghost. What can he do to help people now he is dead?

Name:
Luke Smith
Age:
I6

Chapter 1

If you die young like I did, you don't get to spend much time with your baby brother. I played a lot with my brother Tommy before the crash.

I watched over him after I was dead. I made sure he was safe.

The Christmas he was four, my stepdad
Steve took him to meet Santa in the store.

Chapter 2

A nutter was loose in town. The police had hunted him down, but then lost track of him.

Steve and Tommy saw lots of policemen
outside in the street when they got to the
store.

"What's going on?" Steve asked the policeman standing at the door.

"There's a man with a gun," the policeman said. "We had him but he fired at us and ran off."

Name:
Luke **Smith**
Age:
I6

Chapter 3

There was a line of kids waiting to meet Santa. Steve took Tommy to the toilet first.

"Look!" Tommy said.

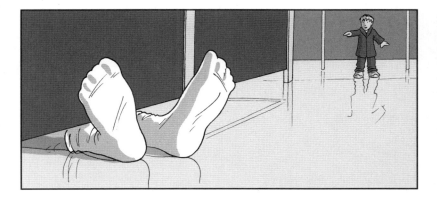

Steve and Tommy could see a man's legs were sticking out under the toilet door.

"Too much drink," Steve said.

Name:
Luke Smith
Age:
I6

Chapter 4

Steve and Tommy went back to the line of kids waiting to see Santa. Soon it was Tommy's turn. Santa sat him on his lap and spoke to him.

"Who are you, little chap?" asked Santa.

"Tommy."

"And what can I do for you today?"

I came up close behind Santa. No one could see me as I am a ghost.

Name:
Luke Smith
Age:
I6

Chapter 5

Something about this Santa was not right. He was too thin for a start. His cloak was much too long. The way he spoke to Tommy was odd.

That's when I knew. The gunman was dressed up as Santa.

A policeman stood up and pointed a gun at Santa and our Tommy.

"Put the kid down and stand up," said the policeman.

"Never," Santa said and held his gun at
Tommy's head.

Name:
Luke Smith
Age:
16

Chapter 6

So the body in the toilet had been the real Santa.

Time to act. I came up behind Tommy and the fake Santa.

"I'm behind you," I said softly in Santa's ear.

He dropped the gun in shock.

"Run!" I said to Tommy.

Tommy ran to Steve. The police moved in on Santa. They had their man. A ghost's whisper was all it took.

Like this book? Why not try the next one?

The Look-out

Luke Smith is dead. But he's back to help those who need it.

Jimmy and Zak are planning to rob Luke's gran.

They'll stop at nothing to get what they want.

What can Luke do to save her?

For more info check out our website:
www.barringtonstoke.co.uk

THE DEAD MAN FILES

Luke Smith is dead. But he's back to help those who need it ...

Watch out for more Dead Man Files coming soon ...

For more info check out our website:
www.barringtonstoke.co.uk